Zebedee's FISH MARKET

ISBN 979-8-88644-196-3 (Paperback)
ISBN 979-8-88644-198-7 (Hardcover)
ISBN 979-8-88644-197-0 (Digital)

Covenant Books
11661 Hwy 707
Murrells Inlet, SC 29576
www.covenantbooks.com

Zebedee's

FISH

MARKET

Keith Boyce

Zebedee was a great fisherman who lived in the land called Galilee in the small village named Capernaum with his wife, Mary Salome, and their sons, James and John.

3

Zebedee, James, and John fished in a large lake called the Sea of Galilee with fishing nets from their boat. Every day before dawn, Zebedee and his sons would set out to the middle of the lake and cast their nets into the water to catch fish. They would then sail down the lake to bring the fish to the market in Tiberius. After delivering their fish, they sailed back home to Capernaum in the late afternoon. The days were long, and the work was hard.

5

When James turned twenty-five, Zebedee decided that he would open his own fish market in Capernaum. James would bring John and a young apprentice fisherman along to help, and the men enjoyed their daily fishing trips. They fished six days a week and were now able to fish both mornings and evenings. On the seventh day, the Sabbath, they rested and worshipped at the great temple in Capernaum.

Zebedee's market was growing quickly. Mary Salome worked at the counter, while Zebedee cleaned the fish on a small table. James and John were catching so many fish that they asked their friends Andrew and Simon Peter to work with them to bring more fish to Zebedee's market. Andrew and Simon Peter were brothers who also lived in Capernaum and always went to the temple with James, John, and their families.

With two boats bringing fish to the market, Zebedee knew that he needed a bigger, stronger butcher block table so that he could keep up with cleaning all of the fish. He also knew that he could ask his friend Joseph to build a new table for him. Joseph lived in Nazareth, and he was a great carpenter. It would be worth the trip to get the perfect table for his fish market.

The next week Zebedee, John, and Simon Peter went to Nazareth to meet with Joseph and order their new table. As Joseph and Zebedee talked about the table, John and Simon Peter talked with Joseph's son Jesus. The young men talked about how one day they would all work together and do great things in the name of God. Joseph and Zebedee finished the plans for the new table, and Joseph promised to deliver it in three weeks. Before they left, Joseph's wife, Mary, fixed a dinner of lamb, bread, and wine for all of them.

Three weeks later, Joseph, Mary, and Jesus brought the big butcher block table to Zebedee's Fish Market in a cart drawn by a donkey. The table was over six feet long and was big enough so that Mary Salome could help clean the fish when she was not busy at the counter.

When the table was set up Mary Salome fixed a huge feast for Joseph, Mary, and Jesus. Zebedee also invited Andrew, Simon Peter, and their parents, Jonah and Joanna. Together, they enjoyed fish caught that morning and several loaves of fresh bread.

15

With the new table and two boats bringing in fish morning and night, Zebedee's Fish Market was now the finest in Galilee. Zebedee was able to get three other fishing boats to bring him fish. This gave the brothers more time to help raise their families since some days they would fish only in the mornings.

With Zebedee's Fish Market doing so well, Andrew and James decided that they would take a short trip for a week to the wilderness near the river Jordan. They had heard the news about a man named John, the cousin of their friend Jesus, who was drawing large crowds at the river.

Andrew and James arrived at the river and saw a man dressed in animal skins who was baptizing many people in the river Jordan. They saw their friend, Jesus, walk up to John and get baptized. As John picked Jesus up out of the river, a beautiful white dove flew over their heads and circled around John and Jesus. James and Andrew knew that they had witnessed something very special.

Later that month, in the late morning, everyone was busy at the fish market. James and John had caught over fifty fish that morning, and Zebedee and Mary were busy preparing them. Andrew and Simon Peter did not have a very good catch, so they decided that they would head back out for a second try. As Andrew finished getting the nets ready, they saw their friend Jesus walking along the Sea of Galilee. Jesus came up to Andrew and Simon Peter and said, "Come follow me, and I will make you fishers of men." The two men dropped everything, including their nets, and followed Jesus.

James and John saw the three men leaving and knew that they too must follow Jesus. They said goodbye to Zebedee and Mary Salome, gave their fishing boat to their apprentice, and went to follow Jesus.

As his sons left, Zebedee held Mary Salome's hand. He did not know where James and John were going, but he put his trust in Jesus knowing that Jesus would show them the way.

About the Author

Keith and his wife, Rosemary, live just outside of Pittsburgh, Pennsylvania. He is very active in his parish with Bible study, men's club, respect life, and jail ministry. Keith and Rosemary love to spend time with their three daughter's families including five grandchildren. Besides being with family, Keith enjoys golf, hiking, theater, and international travel. His love for scripture and the active imaginations of his grandchildren, Reid and Ivy Rose, inspired him to write his first book.

9 798886 441963